david

WHOLE-PERSON HEALTH

'The part can never be well unless the whole is well.'
Plato

'No wonder you are sick. You are not linking yourself enough to the resources that bring healing.'
Selwyn Hughes

First published 2009

Copyright © 2009

British Library Cataloguing in Publication Data. A catalogue record for this book is available from the British Library.

ISBN 978-1-906381-57-8
Published by Autumn House, Grantham, Lincolnshire, England
Printed in Thailand

Bible quotations are taken from the *New International Version* (Hodder and Stoughton) unless otherwise indicated. Other version used: *King James Version*, indicated by the initials KJV.

Whole-person health is not just *physical* health, but *social, mental* and *spiritual* health too. More than that, it recognises the interconnectedness of these four aspects of your health.

Dysfunction in one may cause dysfunction in another, perhaps all.

'Jesus grew in wisdom and stature, and in favour with God and men.'
Luke 2:52

God designed us to grow mentally, physically, spiritually and socially. In this, as in every other respect, Jesus is our exemplar.

The impact on physical health of dysfunction in the social and mental aspects (failure to cope with stress or the tendency to be obsessed by negative thoughts, for example) has been well researched.

Increasingly, these days, attention is drawn to the consequences of our having neglected our spiritual dimension.

God's plans for you are the same
as those of John for his friend:
*'Dear friend, I pray that you may
enjoy good health and that all may
go well with you, even as your soul
is getting along well.'*
3 John 2

'Half the spiritual difficulties that
men and women suffer arise
from a morbid state of health.'
Henry Ward Beecher

God's purposes for you

'I will bring health and healing; . . .
I will heal my people and will let
them enjoy abundant peace and
security.'
Jeremiah 33:6

' "Those who plunder you will be
plundered; all who make spoil of
you I will despoil. But I will restore
you to health and heal your
wounds," declares the Lord.'
Jeremiah 30:16, 17

Charles Darwin demoted humans to the status of animals driven by survival instincts. Karl Marx stressed economic necessity as the driving instinct. Sigmund Freud stressed the sex drive.

Collectively, Darwin, Marx and Freud demoted *mind* and denied *spirit*.

Postmoderns do not lay stress – as 'moderns' did – on 'the grand narratives' built on Darwin-Marx-Freud. They acknowledge *spirit*.

Many contemporary problems can be traced to the aimlessness, meaninglessness and lostness that have resulted from *spiritual* uprootedness.

The media have undermined Christian faith. Destroyed it in many instances. But they have not replaced it.

Nor can they.

Roots!

'I pray that out of [the Father's] glorious riches he may strengthen you with power through his Spirit in your inner being, so that Christ may dwell in your hearts through faith. And I pray that you, being rooted and established in love, may have power, together with all the saints, to grasp how wide and long and high and deep is the love of Christ. . . .'
Ephesians 3:16, 17

Roots anchor us, nourish us and explain us.

'Just as you received Christ Jesus as Lord, continue to live in him, rooted and built up in him, strengthened in the faith. ...' Colossians 2:6, 7

Faith in God gives
you faith in yourself.

The spiritual you
harmonises all the
other aspects of
your living.

Your spirit requires that you be rooted. Psychiatry can investigate and even prune your roots. But Christianity is what provides them.

'Neither is there salvation in any other: for there is none other name under heaven given among men, whereby we must be saved.'
Acts 4:12, KJV

'The name of the Lord is a strong tower; the righteous run to it and are safe.'
Proverbs 18:10

The pilgrim spirit of humanity has a home – a background from which it came, a goal towards which it tends.

That home is God.

You acquire roots through relationship.

The relationship begins
with prayer.

'In everything, by prayer and
petition, with thanksgiving,
present your requests to God.'
Philippians 4:6

For whole-person health
each of the interconnected
aspects of life – physical,
social, mental, spiritual –
need to be in health.

' "For I know the plans I have for you," declares the Lord, "plans to prosper you and not to harm you, plans to give you hope and a future. Then you will call upon me and come and pray to me, and I will listen to you. You will seek me and find me when you seek me with all your heart.'

Jeremiah 29:11-13

'True education means . . . the harmonious development of the physical, the mental, and the spiritual powers. It prepares the student for the joy of service in this world and for the higher joy of wider service in the world to come.'
E. G. White, *Education*, p. 13.

The physical aspect

Dysfunction in the *physical* component is comparatively easy to recognise.

As with social, mental and spiritual health, physical health has a lot to do with lifestyle.

**The major killer diseases
are largely preventable by
adjustments to lifestyle.**

If the upshot of health
research in the last half
century could be reduced
to one sentence, that would
be it.

The killer diseases that stalk your future can be avoided – to a very large degree.

Heart disease and cancer account for 74% of all deaths, for example. We now know that in the great majority of cases these diseases are preventable.

Heart disease, cancer and AIDS account for the vast preponderance of deaths in Africa.

In a great majority of cases, when these diseases have not been inherited, they can be avoided.

It's not down to taking pills. It's down to lifestyle.

Diet is the aspect of lifestyle that many tackle first:

low-fat,
low-sugar,
high-fibre,
low-junk-food,
vegetarian.

Exercise is the aspect of lifestyle we are slower to get around to. Is that because we see some overdoing it? Whatever, it's vital!

You *can* control your cholesterol. You *can* learn how to cope with stress. You *can* cancel your heart attack. You *can* exercise your way back to health. And you most emphatically *can* avoid sexually transmitted diseases.

Body. Mind. Spirit. They interrelate. Your revolution in lifestyle will have to involve them all.

One fantastic thing about the lifestyle approach to whole-person health is that you begin to feel the benefits almost immediately you make the change. Lifestyle adjustments not only prolong the *quantity* of life, but greatly improve life's *quality*.

The benefits of lifestyle change include:

- Greater resistance to minor (as well as major) illnesses.
- A far more positive outlook on life.
- A greater ability to deal with life's problems and problem people.
- *Feeling* – and *being* for all practical purposes – years younger than your actual age.

- Brimful energy that will enable you to perform more effectively in a whole range of physical activities from athletics and sport – to sex.
- Greater fulfilment within the family in leisure activities, and at work.
- A sound sleeping pattern.

The lifestyle revolution will not only enable you to postpone your own funeral. It enables you to live life to the full in the fruitful years you have in store.

The lifestyle revolution needs to involve **the social you** – as well as the physical you. In the same way that some people adjust to living 'a few degrees under par' physically, there are those who never know the meaning of high-level wellness socially. They become accustomed to moods from which they 'suffer'. They accept that not being at ease with other people is 'just me', without digging out a cause.

Their lack of self-confidence
and sense of inferiority –
together with whatever
ways their subconscious
may choose to have them
compensate for these
disabilities socially – are
seen as character traits that
they, and those whose paths
cross theirs, must accept
as the norm and learn to
tolerate.

They cry defeat in the
face of everyday problems.
They struggle and whine
and flounder through their
days with a sense of dull
resentment at life in general
– and the concept of
diagnosis and cure does
not occur to them.

They have a sense of inferiority and inadequacy to the point where it interferes with the attainment of their hopes – and simply do not ask questions.

That unhealthy, destructive private habit of worry so possesses their thinking that shock waves are carried from 'the social' to 'the physical', and soon manifest themselves in all kinds of grisly ways. Fears and phobias frustrate them. Life becomes a travesty of the adventure God intended it to be.

The mental aspect

We live in the fast lane and expect it to be easy street.

We climb a vertical social ladder, and there are definite side effects. Side effects that are *mental.*

The IT revolution has produced whole new personality types, and mental (and physical!) problems. Since leisure, as well as work, is often dominated by the digital, there are consequences. . . .

The most obvious of these consequences is obesity. An exercise-free, desk-jockey's life in which even leisure is absorbed with the screen and the keyboard, is likely to be foreshortened by one of any number of diseases, many of them the consequences of heart disease and high blood pressure. But there are also mental consequences. The constant pursuit of trivial interests and vacant goals.

The sense of aimlessness becomes oppressive. They fear that life has no meaning, and *almost* believe it.

'I am the way and the truth and the life. No one comes to the Father except through me. . . .'
Jesus in John 14:6

'I am the way,' said Jesus.

Have you ever been in a strange
city and asked for directions?
They tend to be complicated
and we get lost before we're
halfway there. If, instead of giving
directions, a person says, 'Come.
I'll take you there', that person,
for us, becomes the way. That's
what Jesus does.

*'Your ears shall hear a word behind
you saying, This is the way, walk in it.'*
Isaiah 30:21

'I am the truth,' Jesus said.

The psalmist said:
*'Teach me your way, O Lord,
and I will walk in your truth.'*
Psalm 86:11

Many men have told us the truth,
but no one except Jesus has
ever embodied it.

'I am the life,' said Jesus.

Jesus was the enfleshment
(incarnation) of God. He
embodied the indestructible life
of the ever-living God. That is why
salvation is found in no one else.

The predominant life-view
these days is that life has no
significance. . . .

Just a pointless pilgrimage
between Point Birth and Point
Death beyond which is eternal
oblivion.

The consciousness that a large
proportion of the brain will never
be utilised, that abilities must
remain unstretched, that the
frustrations of life may be without
significance, must beget tensions
and discords for the mind. . . .

The Christian alternative is based on the Bible. Man is more than one among many species of animal. He was made by God in God's image.

The Bible insists that there *is* a purpose, a meaning, a point and a goal to it all.

The Christian alternative accepts God's book as the foundation of all truth; the personal revelation of a personal Creator who created man to be like himself, and planned that man would live in a special relationship with God himself. On the authority of the Bible, the Christian alternative asserts that man need have no doubts as to where he came from, where he is going to, and what the whole business of life is all about.

The spiritual aspect

Mental attitude is shoved powerfully in a positive direction by our *spiritual* attitude.

It is in the *spiritual* realm that the sense of oppression by the meaninglessness, aimlessness, lostness and rootlessness of postmodern life is painfully acute. But dysfunction in the spiritual area is especially difficult to diagnose, because symptoms take so many forms.

Postmoderns who are also post-Christian suffer spiritual problems because they have lost their way. And not only their way but, arguably, their address. Postmodern sickness is a sickness of the spirit. Once we asked the questions; now we *are* the question.

The Modern era produced the 'grand narratives' (the Darwin-Marx-Freud conventional wisdom) in a more-or-less conscious attempt to supplant Christianity. Postmoderns have rejected the 'grand narratives' but they are aware of the spiritual dimension, have neither totally embraced Christianity nor produced an alternative to it.

To heal diseases of the spirit is to heal the problems of society – *and* to create the harmony between the four components of being necessary for whole-person health.

There is a spiritual *malaise* these days. It is caused by the want of *roots*. To be rooted is the most important and least-recognised need of the human spirit. Roots are the invisible links by which we are held within our spiritual and social context.

There is a want of aim and direction, too. And it is spiritual as well as intellectual.

Next to rootlessness, man's next greatest spiritual disease is *lostness*.

Through prayer and Bible study 'the mind of man is brought into communion with the mind of God, the finite with the Infinite. The effect of such communion on body and mind and soul is beyond estimate.'
Education, page 14.

'The greatest want of the world is the want of men – men who will not be bought or sold, men who in their inmost souls are true and honest, men who do not fear to call sin by its right name, men whose conscience is as true to duty as the needle to the pole, men who will stand for the right though the heavens fall. . . .

'Such a character is not the result of accident; it is not due to special favours or endowments of Providence. A noble character is the result of self-discipline, of the subjection of the lower to the higher nature – the surrender of self for the service of love to God and man.'
Education, page 57.

Lostness

Man lives in a world like an echo-chamber; deafening the ear are demanding, dissonant voices, each trying to shout the loudest. Enticing voices. Strident voices. Persuasive voices.

Words that soothe, words that titillate, words that inflame. Man stands like the subject of a surrealistic fantasy: frantically turning his head, listening to this voice and that, these words and those words, confused, bewildered, spiritually dizzy. Not knowing which way to turn.

Postmoderns represent a generation in which the moral signposts have been broken down, and the frontiers of behaviour rubbed out. Authority is out. Absolutes are out. Behaviourist accounts of thought and conscience are in.

'For the mind and the soul, as well as for the body, it is God's law that strength is acquired by effort. It is exercise that develops. . . . The Bible contains all the principles that men need to understand in order to be fitted either for this life or the life to come. And these principles may be understood by all. . . .'
Education, page 123.

Rootlessness, Aimlessness, Lostness:

All aspects of the disease eating at the heart and entrails of spiritual beings.

But is the disease of 'high-grade malignancy'? Can it be cured or prevented? The diseases of the physical, the social and the mental components of being: can they be prevented or treated?

'The mind occupied with commonplace matters only becomes dwarfed and enfeebled. If never taxed to comprehend grand and far-reaching truths, it after a time loses the power of growth. As a safeguard against this degeneracy and a stimulus to development, nothing else can equal the study of God's Word. . . .'
Education, page 124.

The physical you

Surveys list 'good physical health'
at the top of the priorities of the
majority of people, and 'ill health'
at the top of their list of fears.

The Physical You is the
most complex and exquisitely
fashioned mechanism there
is. No way should it be taken
for granted. But it is.

Even those who prioritise good health can take aspects of it for granted. More often than not they take no account of the long-term effects of lifestyle upon their bodies, so intent are they on getting on, climbing the ladder, winning friends and manipulating people. . . .

For too many people the only concession they make to their health is pill-guzzling. A healthy, balanced diet is of the essence; as is a regular programme of exercise. And remember: **if it doesn't make you sweat, it isn't exercise.**

Remember the World Health Organisation's definition of health:

'Health is a state of complete *physical, mental, social* and *spiritual* well-being; not merely the absence of disease or infirmity.'

Having got that straight, let's pass on to . . .

The social you

Is 'the social you' in good health? Do you 'suffer' from moods? Are you at ease with other people? How is your self-image? Do you lack self-confidence? Do you live with a sense of inferiority?

If so, do you try to cover up your inner feelings of inadequacy by antisocial habits such as talking too much, showing off, playing aloof, acting brusque and hard to handle?

If the answer to any of these questions is 'yes', these things need not be.

Dysfunction in the social component of our being spoils the enjoyment of the whole adventure of life.

Yes, there are great purposes and grand causes; the moral and spiritual dimensions which give living a higher significance. But none of these detracts one jot from the fact that life is meant to be *enjoyed.*

Too many are hampered by an inferiority complex. Yet without a reasonable confidence in your own powers you cannot be successful, and you miss out on the joys of life's adventure. The first step to a cure is to discover the root of your feelings of inferiority. . . .

Basically these feelings arise from a deep, profound self-doubt, and their genesis is in the cobwebbed depths of your past: some emotional violence done to you in childhood, something you did to yourself, the unasked-for circumstances in which you were born, brought up and educated. The roots of the inferiority are more likely to be in *feelings* rather than reasons or objective facts.

Find the root cause and address it. It is suggested that the greatest antidote to the inferiority complex is faith. Repeat the Bible verse: *'I can do everything through him who gives me strength.'* Philippians 4:13

Faith in God gives you faith in yourself. The reason for that is that the Bible is brimful of assurances that to God the value of one soul – for 'one soul' read your name – is beyond all creatures, beyond all institutions, beyond the value of all the world. Never forget it!

How do you acquire faith?

It is a gift from God.

How do you acquire that gift from God?

By communicating with God and allowing God to communicate with you.

How?

First, through prayer. Not surface, formalistic, prayerbook-type prayer. But just you talking to God as to a Friend.

Second, having prayed for help, read God's printed letter to man, the Bible. If you have never read it before, begin with the gospel of Luke in the New Testament. Read it in a modern version like *The New Living Translation.*

In this way, over a period of time, God will fill you with his gift of faith. That done, you will come to realise what your part is in the divine scheme of things and your self-doubts will give way.

Drive your prayers deep into your doubts, fears and 'inferiorities'. When you pray, you are on the hotline to the greatest Power in the universe. Not a shadowy Being in a distant galaxy, but someone by your side . . .

. . . in your office or car or home; always nearby as a Partner. If you fill your mind with affirmations of God's involvement in and concern for your life the dominations of insecurity will be destroyed.

Of course, the problems which weigh us down and make us insecure are not 'all in the mind'. Our lives can hit bad stuff from time to time. We are stuck with the genes we inherit from our parents. There are issues of brain chemistry.

Do not be afraid to discuss these with your physician.

Any fact facing us, however
difficult, is not as important
as our attitude towards the fact.
Victims of the inferiority complex
see all facts through discoloured
attitudes.

Psychiatrist Dr Karl Menninger
has said, 'Attitudes are more
important than facts. . . . Life is
10% what happens and 90% our
attitude to what happens.'

To build up a positive attitude, begin by making a list of all the things you have going for you.

Worry is a destructive private vice. You are not born with it. You let it grow on you. The effects of worry carry over into all four spheres of life, especially the physical and the social.

Worry is founded on fear, and fear can only be overcome by faith.

Faith masters fear.
And, remember, you receive
the gift of faith by spending time
each day with God. Worry is a
cancer that spreads through the
mind and fills it with thoughts
contrary to God's care.

Cancel each day as you scrunch a page of your calendar. Live a day at a time, 'forgetting what is behind and straining towards what is ahead'. Philippians 3:13

Inch by inch, life's a cynch. Yard by yard, it's hard.

Expel worry. Fill your mind with thoughts of God's power, God's protection, God's goodness, God's grace.

'Don't waste your life fretting,' (Psalm 37:1) a wise man said. That means adopting a different lifestyle.

That leads to a change in the character of your thoughts. Over-stimulation, fatigue, frustration, debilitation, even emotional illness, result from the ultrasonic pace of our lives.

Slow down, and receive
'the peace of God, which
transcends all understanding.'
Philippians 4:7

Relax, and receive the peace
of God – into your joints, as
well as into every facet of
your personality.

Choice

At some level you always have a *choice* of attitude. Choose to be happy. Reject – don't harbour – negative feelings.

Choose a positive outlook, and your social life will blossom; you will enjoy the adventure of living – even become well-liked, and feel an all-pervasive sense of well-being. In short, the social component of your being will be 100% healthy.

The intellectual you

Don't be put off by the word 'intellectual'.

The part if you we are talking about is the part that thinks – *the mind*. It is the aspect of your makeup which, though often suppressed, is searching for answers to life's questions. . . .

. . . Looking for a sense of purpose, fulfilment; and yearning for firsthand experience that makes your life a meaningful adventure.

The intellectual you cries out to be challenged, to pursue some great goal with enthusiasm, and rebels against the boredom of life.

Man's most obvious missing component is a built-in direction finder, a psychological equivalent of the automatic pilot. And without aim there is no challenge.

Jesus saw how empty, pointless existence left the spirit of man like an empty house – a prey to invasion by despondency, despair and mental turmoil. He put forward a dominating life-fulfilling purpose: salvation by grace through faith – in him.

Jesus knew that rich talent lies buried beneath the soil of self-pity and injured self-importance. To him the individual was of supreme importance.

Jesus set each human life against the background of eternity, extending to an infinite perspective each individual struggle for worth and hope.

Jesus never spoke in terms of large-sounding abstractions like 'humanity' and 'mankind'. He always spoke of you and you and you. Within God's great purpose every person's life-work makes its own unique contribution. Accept his leadership and you accept adventure and reject futility.

In the hectic, noisy pattern of life these days, a daily 'quiet time' can have a strong therapeutic value. For minds in turmoil, this daily practice of silence can bring peace.

When you practise silence, don't read, don't write, don't worry. And after your period of silence, pray that the tensions of life may be kept at bay and the inner harmony of mind may be restored.

Reject futility and begin 'great things', the supreme adventure into which Jesus Christ invites you.

The spiritual you

The spiritual you harmonises all
the other aspects of your living.
Unless the spiritual you is at
peace, you are a walking civil war.

And if you do not recognise
the existence of a 'spiritual you',
you are seriously underestimating
your importance and the
significance of your life.

If you deny the spirit, you are close to the Darwin-Marx-Freud 'received wisdom' about man as an animal led by the nose by his instincts.

Remember, dysfunction in the spiritual you is often caused by a sense of 'uprootedness'. Arnold Wesker once wrote, 'Roots, the things you come from, the things that feed you, the things that make you proud of yourself. . . .'

Psychiatry is a highly developed skill in root investigation and root pruning. But of vaster importance: Christianity has to do with the root system of the individual.

Christianity is the permanent soil from which the root system draws thought, aspiration, belonging, aim, self-respect, stability, feeling and worth.

We move and grow and journey –
and may even pass from the
scene – but we have roots among
eternal things.

Those roots remain though all
else changes. A person's spiritual
being develops as he grows.
Those roots are in a loving
Creator-God who cares and
guides and empathises.

Those roots go down to the nourishing stream of God's grace expressed through the life and death and resurrection of Jesus, his Son.

The pilgrim spirit of humanity has a home, a background from whence it came, a goal towards which it tends.

For whole-person health, the spiritual you requires a faith in a caring God, an assurance of his salvation, the moral shelter of his code for living and the deep emotional resource and comfort of divine love which knows no limit.

When the spiritual you is rooted in God, the diseases and dysfunctions of the spirit require no healing. Your problems are offloaded on broader shoulders than your own.

You are no longer lost. God has found you. And in him your life has meaning.

In him you have peace and joy: a peace that passes understanding and a joy that no man can take from you.

For whole-person health each of the interrelated aspects of being – the physical, the social, the intellectual and the spiritual – needs to be in health.

And basic to all is the spiritual.

'Man, created for fellowship with God, can only in such fellowship find his real life and development. Created to find in God his highest joy, he can find in nothing else that which can quiet the cravings of the heart, can satisfy the hunger and thirst of the soul.' *Education,* pages 124, 125

Christ's invitation

*'Come to me, all you who are weary and
burdened, and I will give you rest. Take
my yoke upon you and learn from me,
for I am gentle and humble in heart,
and you will find rest for your souls....'*
Jesus in Matthew 11:28, 29.

Anyone, any place, any time, who
comes to Jesus is always, always,
always accepted. He saves to the
uttermost and the outermost.

*'He is able to save them to the
uttermost that come unto God
by him.'*
Hebrews 7:25, KJV

When death strikes close by,
remember Jesus was not just
resurrected, he *is* the resurrection
and the life, and personally
guarantees that those who
die committed to his cause
will live again.

*'I am the resurrection and the
life. He who believes in me will
live, even though he dies; and
whoever lives and believes in
me will never die.'*
John 11:25, 26

We may tire, grow weary, stumble and fall. But if we depend on the Lord for strength we may yet soar.

'Those who hope in the Lord will renew their strength. They will soar on wings like eagles; they will run and not grow weary, they will walk and not be faint.'
Isaiah 40:31

There are anxious times for us all. There are times of weakness. But in those times God carries us.

'Cast all your anxiety on him because he cares for you.'
1 Peter 5:7

'Why are you downcast,
O my soul?
Why so disturbed within me?
Put your hope in God,
for I will yet praise him,
my Saviour and my God.'
Psalm 42:11

'There is a God-shaped blank
in every man's mind.
If a man is not made for God,
why is he happy only in God?
If a man is made for God, why
is he opposed to God?'
Blaise Pascal

'The essential fact of Christianity is that God thought all men worth the sacrifice of his Son.

'The fact of Jesus coming is the final and unanswerable proof that God cares.

'Jesus commended the poor in spirit. The man who is poor in spirit is the man who has realised that things mean nothing, and that God means everything.'
William Barclay

'Death, that final curb on freedom, has itself suffered a death blow through the resurrection of Jesus.'
Michael Green

'Death be not proud, though some have called thee
Mighty and dreadful, for thou art not so,
For those whom thou think'st thou dost overthrow,
Die not, poor death, nor yet canst thou kill me. . . .
One short sleep past, we wake eternally,
And Death shall be no more: Death, thou shalt die!'
John Donne (1573-1631)

'God is our refuge and strength,
an ever-present help in trouble.
Therefore we will not fear, though
the earth give way and the
mountains fall into the heart of
the sea, though its waters roar
and foam and the mountains quake
with their surging. There is a river
whose streams make glad the city
of God, the holy place where the
Most High dwells. God is within
her, she will not fall. . . .'
Psalm 46:1-5

'God cannot give us happiness and peace apart from himself, because it is not there. There is no such thing. . . . God whispers in our pleasures but shouts in our pain. When pain is to be borne, a little courage helps more than much knowledge, a little human sympathy more than much courage, and the least tincture of the love of God more than all.'
C. S. Lewis

'The Gospel is open to all; the most respectable sinner has no more claim on it than the worst.

'Faith always shows itself in the whole personality.

'Whatever may happen to you, God is your Father, and he is interested in you, and that is his attitude towards you.

'The glory of the Gospel is that when the church is absolutely different from the world, she invariably attracts it.'
David Martyn Lloyd-Jones

'Man is always a unity. He is body, and he is mind and soul; and he *can* be spirit.

'Life is filled with meaning as soon as Jesus Christ enters into it.

'The purpose of revelation is restoration, the renewal in us of that likeness to God which man lost by sin.'
Stephen Neill

'All men who live with any degree of serenity live by some assurance of grace.'
Reinhold Niebuhr

'In our revelation, God is the agent as well as the object. It is not just that men speak about God, or for God; God speaks for himself, and talks to us in person.

'God the Father is the giver of Holy Scripture; God the Son is the theme of Holy Scripture; and God the Spirit is the Author, authenticator and interpreter of Holy Scripture.'
James I. Packer

'Man, made in the image of God, has a purpose – to be in a relationship to God, who is there. Man forgets his purpose and thus he forgets who he is and what life means.'
Francis Schaeffer

'Grace strikes us when we are in great pain and restlessness. It strikes us when we walk through the dark valley of a meaningless and empty life. It strikes us when we feel that our separation is deeper than usual.'
Paul Tillich

'Grace is love that cares and stoops and rescues.'
John Stott

'Goodness is stronger than evil;
Love is stronger than hate;
Light is stronger than darkness;
Life is stronger than death;
Victory is ours through him who
loved us.'
Desmond Tutu

Prayers for the sick

Lord God,
This illness is making me depressed.
I am irritated by its aches and pains.
I get tired of doing nothing.
I worry about the extra work I am
causing others.
O God,
Speak to me in the quietness about
your majesty,
The wonder and beauty of your creation,
About your love for me.
Speak to me about Jesus Christ my
Saviour –
The pain of Calvary, about his
resurrection life.
O God, I will worship you.
Thomas Fuller

From the depths of my despair I
call to you, Lord.
Hear my cry, O Lord;
Listen to my call for help!
I wait eagerly for the Lord's help
And in his word I trust.
From Psalm 130

Father, lover of life, we pray for
those suffering from disease
for which, at present, there is
no known cure; give them
confidence in your love and
never-failing support and a
stronger faith in the resurrection.
Grant wisdom and perseverance
to all working to discover the
causes of the disease, so that
they see in their labours the
ministry of your Son, who himself
showed forth his divine power by
healing those who came to him.
George Appleton

Lord, we pray for all who are weighed down with the mystery of suffering. Reveal yourself to them as the God of love, who yourself bear all our suffering.
George Appleton

Lord of great compassion,
we pray you for those who
are nervously ill, and too weak
and anxious to lift themselves
above the fear and sadness
that threaten to overwhelm them.
Do you yourself, O Lord, lift them
up and deliver them, as you
delivered your disciples in the
storm at sea, strengthening their
faith and banishing their fear.
Elizabeth Goudge

Father, we pray for the mentally ill, for all who are of a disturbed and troubled mind. Be to them light in their darkness, their refuge and strength in time of fear. Give special skills and tender hearts to all who care for them, and show them how best to assist in your work of healing; through Jesus Christ our Lord. *Timothy Dudley-Smith*

O God the Creator and Father of all men, We praise you that your will is life and health and strength. Help all who are ill or in pain to place themselves in your hands in loving trust, so that your healing life may flow into them to make them well and strong, able and ready to do your holy will; through him who has made known to us both your love and your will, even Jesus Christ our Lord.

George Appleton

Lord, comfort the sick, the hungry,
the lonely and those who are hurt
and shut in on themselves, by
your presence in their hearts; use
us to help them in a practical way.
Show us how to set about this
and give us strength, tact and
compassion.
Etta Gullick

O God of love and power, we come to you for those who are ill in body or mind, and for those who are cast down and sad. Tell them in the midst of all their pain and anxiety that your name is Love; and since you have ordained that your own will needs our co-operation, use these our prayers. Turn our caring into their courage, our solicitude into their succour, our faith into their will to get well; through Jesus Christ our Lord.

Leslie D. Weatherhead

O God our Father, who are the source of all life and health, all strength and peace: Teach us to know you truly; take from us all that hinders the work of your healing power, all our sins, all our anxieties and fears, all resentment and hardness of heart; and help us to learn to enter into stillness and peace with you, and to know that you are our healer and redeemer.

Guild of Health

What is man that you have been
   mindful of him,
Mortal man that you have taken
   note of him,
That you have made him little less
   than divine
And adorned him with glory and
   majesty;
You have made him master over
   your handiwork,
Laying the world at his feet?
*Psalm 8:5-7 (from a Jewish
translation)*

The Lord is my shepherd:
therefore can I lack nothing.
He shall feed me in a green
pasture: and lead me forth beside
the waters of comfort.
He shall convert my soul:
and bring me forth in the paths
of righteousness, for his Name's
sake.
Yea, though I walk through
the valley of the shadow of death,
I will fear no evil: for thou art
with me; thy rod and thy staff
comfort me.

Psalm 23 in the Oxford Book of Prayer

Have mercy upon me, O God,
after thy great goodness:
according to the multitude of thy
mercies do away mine offences.
Wash me thoroughly from my
wickedness: and cleanse me
from my sin . . .
But lo, thou requirest truth in the
inward parts: and shalt make me
to understand wisdom secretly . . .
Make me a clean heart, O God:
and renew a right spirit within me.
Cast me not away from thy
presence: and take not thy holy
Spirit from me.
Psalm 51 in the Oxford Book of Prayer